Developing Num

MENTAL MATHS

ACTIVITIES FOR THE DAILY MATHS LESSON

year
3

Hilary Koll and Steve Mills

A & C BLACK

Contents

Recall of known facts (x and ÷)

Mental calculation strategies (x and ÷)

Published 2004 by A & C Black Publishers Limited
37 Soho Square, London W1D 3QZ
www.acblack.com

ISBN 0-7136-6912-8

Copyright text © Hilary Koll and Steve Mills, 2004
Copyright illustrations © Kirsty Wilson, 2004
Copyright cover illustration © Charlotte Hard, 2004
Editors: Lynne Williamson and Marie Lister

The authors and publishers would like to thank Jane McNeill and Catherine Yemm for their advice in producing this series of books.

A CIP catalogue record for this book is available from the British Library.

Printed and bound in Great Britain by Cromwell Press Ltd, Trowbridge.

A & C Black uses paper produced with elemental chlorine-free pulp, harvested from managed sustainable forests.

Introduction

Developing Numeracy: Mental Maths is a series of seven photocopiable activity books designed to be used during the daily maths lesson. This book focuses on the skills and concepts for mental maths outlined in the National Numeracy Strategy *Framework for teaching mathematics* for Year 3. The activities are intended to be used in the time allocated to pupil activities; they aim to reinforce the knowledge and develop the facts, skills and understanding explored during the main part of the lesson. They provide practice and consolidation of the objectives contained in the framework document.

Mental Maths Year 3

To calculate mentally with confidence, it is necessary to understand the three main aspects of numeracy shown in the diagram below. These underpin the teaching of specific mental calculation strategies.

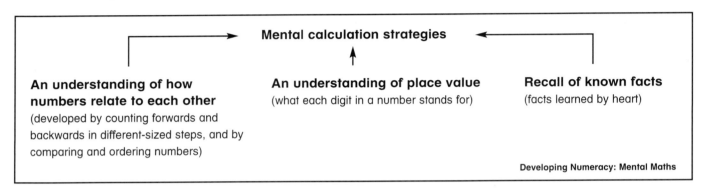

Mental calculation strategies

An understanding of how numbers relate to each other (developed by counting forwards and backwards in different-sized steps, and by comparing and ordering numbers)

An understanding of place value (what each digit in a number stands for)

Recall of known facts (facts learned by heart)

Developing Numeracy: Mental Maths

Year 3 supports the teaching of mental maths by providing a series of activities which develop these essential skills. On the whole the activities are designed for children to work on independently, although this is not always possible and occasionally some children may need support.

Year 3 develops concepts and skills for the different aspects of numeracy in the following ways:

An understanding of how numbers relate to each other

- counting on and back in steps of 2, 3, 4, 5, 10, 20 and 100;
- comparing two given three-digit numbers, saying which is more or less, and giving a number which lies between them.

An understanding of place value

- knowing what each digit represents, and partitioning three-digit numbers into hundreds, tens and ones (HTU);
- saying the number that is 1, 10 or 100 more/less than any given two- or three-digit number.

Recall of known facts

Know by heart or derive quickly:

- all addition facts for each number to 20;
- all subtraction facts for each number to 20;
- all pairs of multiples of 100 with a total of 1000;
- all pairs of multiples of 5 with a total of 100;
- multiplication facts for the 2, 3, 4, 5 and 10 times tables, and the corresponding division facts;
- doubles of all numbers to 20 and halves of all even numbers to 40;
- doubles of multiples of 5 to 100;
- doubles of multiples of 50 to 500, and all the corresponding halves.

Mental calculation strategies

- putting the larger number first and counting on in tens and ones;
- adding more than two numbers;
- partitioning into '5 and a bit' or tens and units when adding, then recombining;
- finding a small difference by counting up;
- identifying near doubles, using doubles already known;
- adding or subtracting near multiples of 10 by adding or subtracting the multiples of 10, then adjusting;
- using patterns of similar calculations;
- using known number facts and place value to add or subtract pairs of numbers mentally;
- using doubling or halving, starting from known facts;
- using known number facts and place value to carry out mentally simple multiplications and divisions.

Extension

Many of the activity sheets end with a challenge (**Now try this!**) which reinforces and extends the children's learning, and provides the teacher with an opportunity for assessment. On

occasion it may be helpful to read the instructions with the children before they begin the activity. For some of the challenges the children will need to record their answers on a separate piece of paper.

Organisation

Very little equipment is needed, but it will be useful to have the following resources available: coloured pencils, counters, dice, scissors, coins, number lines and number tracks.

To help teachers select appropriate learning experiences for the children, the activities are grouped into sections within the book. However, the activities are not expected to be used in this order; the sheets are intended to support, rather than direct, the teacher's planning.

Some activities can be made easier or more challenging by masking or substituting numbers. You may wish to re-use some pages by copying them onto card and laminating them.

Teachers' notes

Brief notes are provided at the foot of each page giving ideas and suggestions for maximising the effectiveness of the activity sheets. These can be masked before copying.

Whole-class warm-up activities

The following activities provide some practical ideas which can be used to introduce the main teaching part of the lesson.

Poster numbers

Write all the multiples of 5 up to 50 on a poster, in random order. Call out questions (for example, *5 times 8; 6 multiplied by 5; 5 lots of 3*) and ask the children to find the answers on the poster.

20		35	
	15		40
10		25	
	30		45
5		50	

Other posters might show:
- all multiples of 5 up to 100. Give the children one number and ask them to find its partner to 100: for example, *What adds to 25 to make 100?* Alternatively, ask for pairs of numbers that total 100.
- the numbers 1 to 20. Give the children one number and ask them to find its partner to 20: for example, *What adds to 12 to make 20?* Alternatively, ask for pairs of numbers that total 20. Also with the numbers 1 to 20, say a number (such as 25 or 44) and ask the children to find three numbers that add to make this number: for example, 25 = 7 + 8 + 10. Ask: *Can you find another way of making 25?*

Function machines

Draw a simple machine on the board and write a single-step or multi-step operation inside it, such as '+ 5' or '× 3 − 2'. Say a number and ask for the output number after the rule has been applied.

Function machines can also be used in the following ways:
- give the output number and ask the children for the input number that produces it;
- give pairs of input and output numbers that correspond to the same rule, and ask the children to work out the rule.

Missing numbers

Write some number statements on the board, using a box in the place of one of the numbers in the question: for example, 28 − ☐ = 19, ☐ + 29 = 58. Invite children to come and fill in the missing numbers.

Targets

Write several numbers on the board, such as 100, 50, 10, 6, 4, 3, and a target number, such as 550. Set the children the challenge of hitting the target number, or getting as close as possible to it, using some or all of the numbers and whatever operations they wish. A solution to this example is: 6 + 3 = 9; 9 × 50 = 450; 450 + 100 = 550.

Path finder

- Use a different-coloured pencil to draw each path.
  The first one has been started for you.

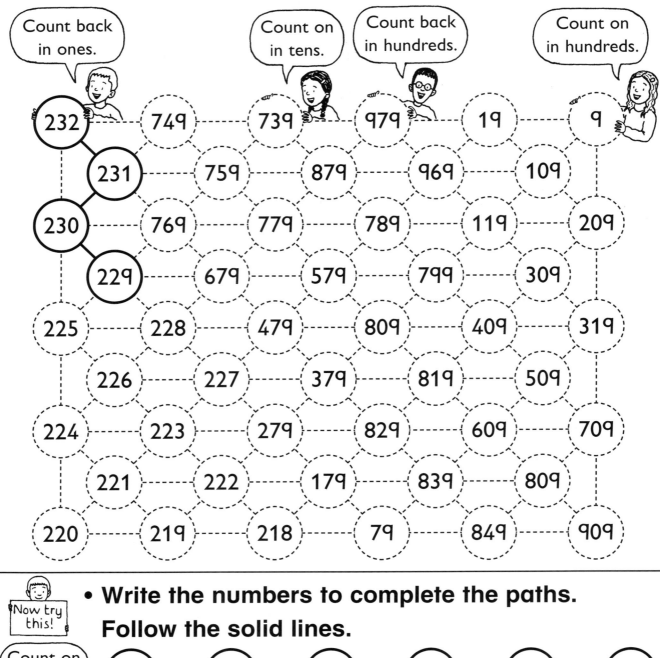

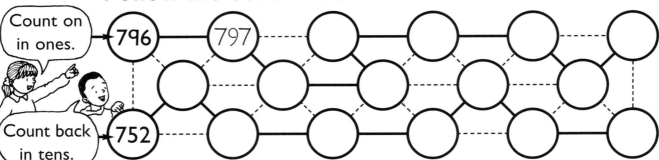

- Write the numbers to complete the paths.
  Follow the solid lines.

Teachers' note Explain to the children that some routes may cross, so not to colour in the circles. Ask them to read each sequence aloud to reinforce the patterns and to draw attention to which digit is changing each time.

Developing Numeracy
Mental Maths Year 3
© A & C BLACK

Cheerleaders

The cheerleaders count around the circle in [twos].

Jo — Beth — Daisy — Kim — Ella — Asma — Leah — Chloe

1. If Jo shouts [zero], who will shout these numbers?

(a) 24 _____   (b) 40 _____

(c) 58 _____   (d) 74 _____

(e) 82 _____   (f) 98 _____

2. If Jo shouts [one], who will shout these numbers?

(a) 15 _____   (b) 39 _____

(c) 45 _____   (d) 73 _____

(e) 87 _____   (f) 99 _____

Now try this!

Now Jo shouts [100]. **The cheerleaders count back in twos to zero.**

• **Write all the numbers Ella will shout.**

_____

Teachers' note At the start of the lesson, try this activity practically with the class, counting on and back in twos. When completing the sheet, encourage the children to count around the circle in the picture, pointing to each cheerleader in turn. The numbers can be changed to provide further questions for more confident children, or the children could be asked to count around in steps of other sizes.

Developing Numeracy
Mental Maths Year 3
© A & C BLACK

Hit the target

- **Play this game with a partner.**

☆ Cut out the cards. Place the instruction cards in a pile, face down. Then choose a target number.

☆ Take turns to pick up an instruction card. Say the number sequence aloud. If the target number is in your sequence, score a point.

☆ When you have used all the instruction cards, add up your scores.

☆ Shuffle the instruction cards and pick a new target number. Play the game again.

 **35**  **46**  **50**  **41**  **54**  **59**

Start at 27. Count on in threes. Stop at 60.	Start at 26. Count on in fours. Stop at 58.	Start at 24. Count on in fives. Stop at 64.
Start at 29. Count on in threes. Stop at 62.	Start at 31. Count on in fours. Stop at 63.	Start at 33. Count on in fives. Stop at 63.
Start at 31. Count on in threes. Stop at 55.	Start at 27. Count on in fours. Stop at 55.	Start at 21. Count on in fives. Stop at 61.
Start at 33. Count on in threes. Stop at 63.	Start at 30. Count on in fours. Stop at 62.	Start at 22. Count on in fives. Stop at 62.

Teachers' note The children can check each other's sequences on a number line or using the constant function on a calculator: for example, 27 ⊞ ⊞ 3 ⊟ ⊟ ⊟ ⊟ ⊟ ⊟… As an extension activity, ask the children to find out which sequences contain the number 48 by writing out the sequences on the back of the cards.

**Developing Numeracy
Mental Maths Year 3
© A & C BLACK**

8

Puzzle it out

- **Find the circled number in the puzzle. Follow the instructions.**

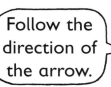 
Follow the direction of the arrow.

(1) ~~Count back in 3s~~   (2) Count back in 4s   (3) Count back in 4s

(4) Count back in 3s   (5) Count on in 2s   (6) Count on in 5s

(7) Count back in 4s   (8) Count back in 5s   (9) Count on in 5s

(10) Count on in 4s   (11) Count on in 5s   (12) Count back in 4s

(13) Count on in 5s   (14) Count on in 5s   (15) Count on in 20s

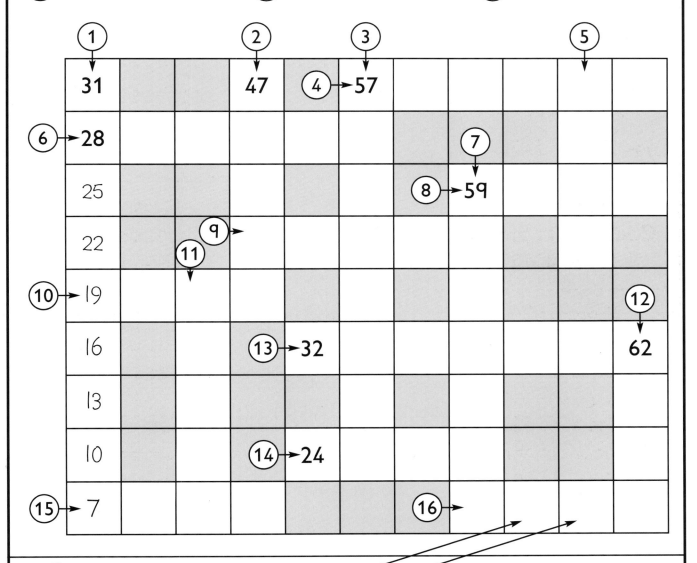

- **Fill in these two numbers to make a sequence. Write the rule for sequence (16).**

Teachers' note Discuss how to complete the grid and encourage the children to cross off each instruction as they go. Point out that some instructions involve counting on and some involve counting back. Some children may find number lines or 100-squares helpful for finding numbers or checking their answers.

**Developing Numeracy
Mental Maths Year 3
© A & C BLACK**

Abacus beads

- **Shade the correct number of beads on the abacus.**

  Then split the number into hundreds, tens and units.

1.

900	90	9
800	80	8
700	70	7
600	60	6
500	50	5
400	40	4
300	30	3
200	20	2
100	10	1

5   4   7

$500 + 40 + 7$

2.

900	90	9
800	80	8
700	70	7
600	60	6
500	50	5
400	40	4
300	30	3
200	20	2
100	10	1

2   6   1

_____

3.

900	90	9
800	80	8
700	70	7
600	60	6
500	50	5
400	40	4
300	30	3
200	20	2
100	10	1

7   2   9

_____

4.

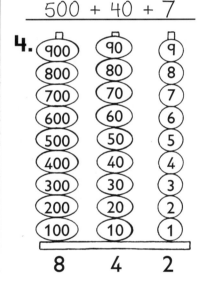

8   4   2

_____

5.

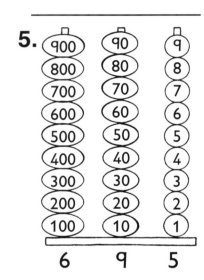

6   9   5

_____

6.

900	90	9
800	80	8
700	70	7
600	60	6
500	50	5
400	40	4
300	30	3
200	20	2
100	10	1

3   7   8

_____

Now try this!

- **Split these numbers in the same way.**

$627 = \underline{\quad 600 + 20 + 7 \quad}$ $886 = \underline{\qquad\qquad}$

$512 = \underline{\qquad\qquad}$ $397 = \underline{\qquad\qquad}$

$745 = \underline{\qquad\qquad}$ $168 = \underline{\qquad\qquad}$

$693 = \underline{\qquad\qquad}$ $372 = \underline{\qquad\qquad}$

$380 = \underline{\qquad\qquad}$ $709 = \underline{\qquad\qquad}$

$801 = \underline{\qquad\qquad}$ $510 = \underline{\qquad\qquad}$

Teachers' note This activity helps children to understand the different values of the digits in a three-digit number. In the extension activity, remind the children of the value of each column of abacus beads. Use a real abacus to reinforce these ideas, again stressing the different values of the columns.

**Developing Numeracy
Mental Maths Year 3
© A & C BLACK**

Pizza creations

☆ Place a counter anywhere on each pizza. Create a three-digit number, like this:

• roll the dice and move the 100s counter
• roll again and move the 10s counter
• roll again and move the 1s counter.

You need:
• three small counters
• a dice

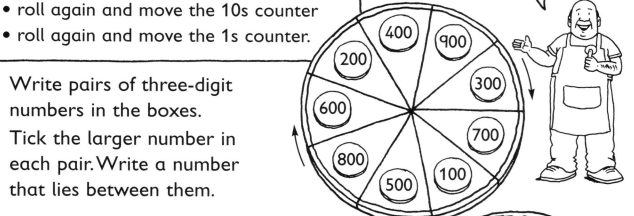

☆ Write pairs of three-digit numbers in the boxes.

☆ Tick the larger number in each pair. Write a number that lies between them.

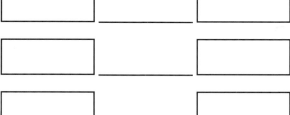

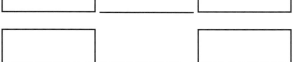

Now try this!

• **Which three whole numbers match this description?**

_____

It is larger than 492 and smaller than 504. Two of its digits are the same.

Teachers' note Explain that the children who create the largest and smallest three-digit numbers are the winners. Ask the children to talk in pairs about how to decide which number in a pair is larger (for example, if the hundreds digits are not the same, comparing the hundreds digits tells you which number is larger).

Developing Numeracy
Mental Maths Year 3
© A & C BLACK

Rainbow petals

☆ **You need** six coloured pencils.

☆ In the key, shade each box a different colour.

☆ Compare each number on the petals with the centre number. How many more or less is it? Colour the petals using the key.

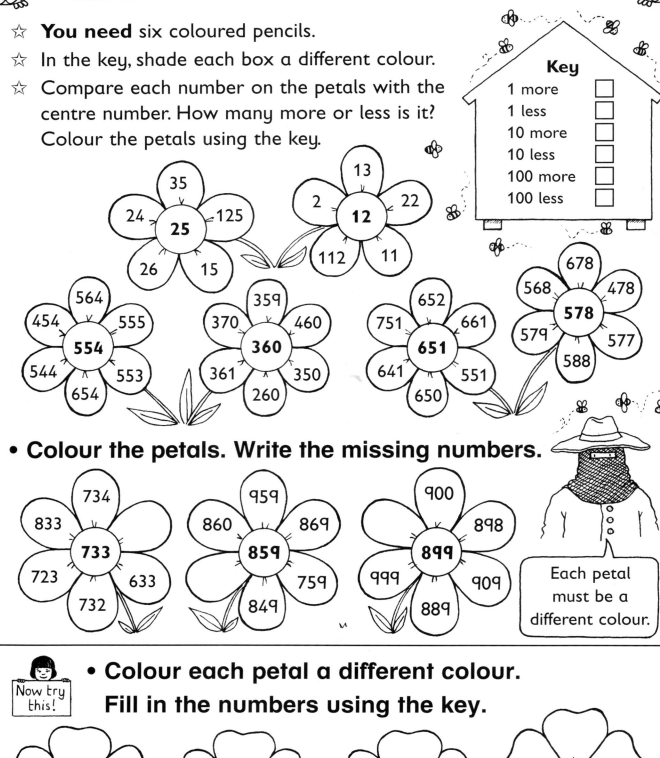

Key

1 more	☐
1 less	☐
10 more	☐
10 less	☐
100 more	☐
100 less	☐

Flower 1 (centre **25**): 35, 24, 125, 26, 15

Flower 2 (centre **12**): 13, 2, 22, 112, 11

Flower 3 (centre **554**): 564, 454, 555, 544, 553, 654

Flower 4 (centre **360**): 359, 370, 460, 361, 350, 260

Flower 5 (centre **651**): 652, 751, 661, 641, 551, 650

Flower 6 (centre **578**): 678, 568, 478, 579, 577, 588

• **Colour the petals. Write the missing numbers.**

Flower (centre **733**): 734, 833, 723, 633, 732

Flower (centre **859**): 959, 860, 869, 759, 849

Flower (centre **899**): 900, 898, 999, 909, 889

Each petal must be a different colour.

• **Colour each petal a different colour. Fill in the numbers using the key.**

Now try this!

Flower centres: **430**, **211**, **106**, **689**

Teachers' note At the start of the lesson, discuss the effect of adding and subtracting 1, 10 or 100 to/from two- and three-digit numbers (for example, when adding 10 to 529 the only digit to change is the tens digit, which increases by one). Some children may find it helpful to use place value (arrow) cards to partition the numbers before adding or subtracting.

Developing Numeracy Mental Maths Year 3 © A & C BLACK

Dog show

- **Write the numbers in order on the dogs. Start with the smallest number.**

1.
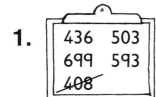
436	503
699	593
408	

408

2.
312	409
280	534
78	

3.
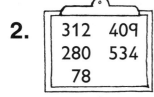
718	498
721	399
69	

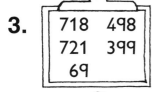

4.
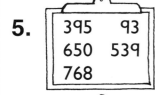
507	198
854	523
692	

5.
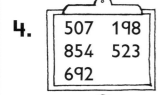
395	93
650	539
768	

6.
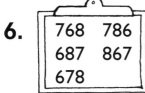
768	786
687	867
678	

Now try this!

- **Mark these numbers on the number lines.**

| 25 | 47 | 92 |

0   100

25

| 700 | 350 | 25 |

0   1000

Teachers' note Remind the children that when comparing three-digit numbers, they should start with the digit furthest to the left. If two numbers have the same hundreds digit, compare the tens digits. If the numbers have the same hundreds and tens digits, then compare the units digits.

**Developing Numeracy
Mental Maths Year 3
© A & C BLACK**

What's on the menu?

- **Write the answer on each molehill.**
- **Colour the questions with the answer** $\boxed{19}$
  to show how the mole reaches his favourite food.

5 + 8   1 + 12   9 + 11

7 + 12   19   7 + 6   5 + 15   5 + 13

6 + 8   6 + 6   9 + 8   2 + 10

9 + 10   4 + 12   8 + 8   12 + 4

4 + 5   11 + 8   18 + 1   6 + 9   4 + 7

8 + 9   6 + 13   3 + 16

1 + 17   8 + 3   7 + 13   7 + 9

12 + 8   7 + 11   14 + 5   0 + 18

6 + 5   4 + 16   3 + 12   7 + 12

13 + 5   9 + 6   17 + 2   14 + 2

14 + 0   15 + 3   4 + 15   1 + 19

16 + 2   8 + 10   2 + 15   6 + 10

11 + 5   2 + 18   10 + 9   8 + 12

3 + 14   7 + 7   5 + 14   3 + 13

9 + 4   9 + 6   11 + 6   17 + 1

8 + 7   8 + 12   13 + 6   9 + 9

Now try this!

- **Write nine pairs of numbers with a total of** $\boxed{17}$.

Teachers' note Encourage the children to recall the answers or to use related facts that will help them find the answer, rather than using counting on methods. When they have completed the activity, ask them to read questions and answers aloud, using a range of vocabulary: for example, 'If I add 7 to 12 I get 19'; '7 plus 8 equals 15'; 'The total/sum of 12 and 4 is 16'.

**Developing Numeracy
Mental Maths Year 3
© A & C BLACK**

Monster feet

• **Write the answers on the toenails.**

1.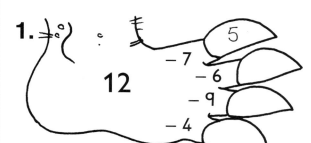

12   − 7   5
      − 6
      − 9
      − 4

2.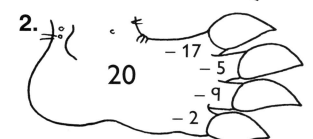

20   − 17
      − 5
      − 9
      − 2

3.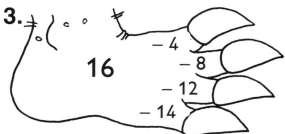

16   − 4
      − 8
      − 12
      − 14

4.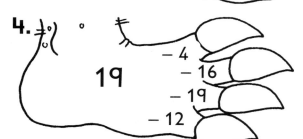

19   − 4
      − 16
      − 19
      − 12

5.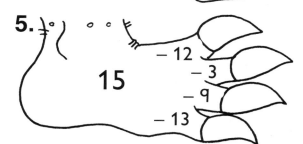

15   − 12
      − 3
      − 9
      − 13

6.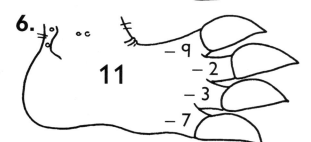

11   − 9
      − 2
      − 3
      − 7

7.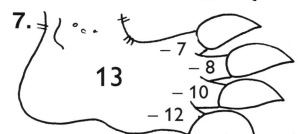

13   − 7
      − 8
      − 10
      − 12

8.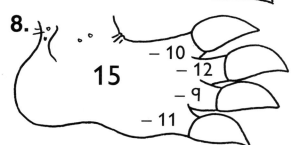

15   − 10
      − 12
      − 9
      − 11

9.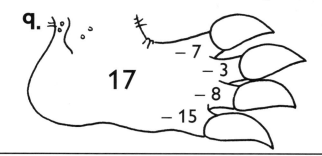

17   − 7
      − 3
      − 8
      − 15

Now try this!

• **List subtraction facts which start with the number** 18 **. Find as many as you can.**

Example: $18 - 0 = 18$ $18 - 1 =$

Teachers' note Encourage the children to recall the answers or to use related facts that will help them find the answer, rather than using counting on or back methods. When they have completed the activity, ask them to read questions and answers aloud, using a range of vocabulary: for example, 'If I subtract 7 from 12 I get 5'; '20 take away 9 is 11'.

Developing Numeracy
Mental Maths Year 3
© A & C BLACK

25

Birthday badges

In each question, the ages of the two people total 100.

- Write the missing ages. Check your answers by adding the two numbers together.

1. 90   10

2. 30

3. 60

4. 50

5. 20

6. 95

7. 45

8. 25

9. 65

10. 15

11. 35

12. 55

Now try this!

- Complete these as quickly as you can.

$100 - 40 = \boxed{}$ $\boxed{} + 75 = 100$ $100 - 85 = \boxed{}$

$100 - \boxed{} = 35$ $100 - \boxed{} = 5$ $65 + \boxed{} = 100$

Teachers' note Encourage the children to use their knowledge of number pairs with a total of 10 (for example, 4 + 6 = 10 so 40 + 60 = 100). Point out that when adding numbers ending in 5, the units digits add to make 10, so the tens must total 90. Watch out for children making mistakes such as 45 + 65 = 100.

**Developing Numeracy
Mental Maths Year 3
© A & C BLACK**

Soup for dinner

- **Work out how much soup each person has altogether.**
  Count on from the larger number.

1.

Start with 136 and count on 9.

9 ml + 136 ml = _____ ml

2.

6 ml + 175 ml = _____ ml

3.

4 ml + 367 ml = _____ ml

4.

438 ml + 7 ml = _____ ml

5.

732 ml + 9 ml = _____ ml

6.

8 ml + 605 ml = _____ ml

7.

7 ml + 896 ml = _____ ml

8.

6 ml + 995 ml = _____ ml

Now try this!

- **Choose a grey card and a white card.**
- **Add the numbers and write the addition.**
- **Make as many different totals as you can.**

| 4 | 9 | 7 | 11 | | 314 | 636 | 531 |

Teachers' note Discuss why it is easier to count on from the larger number when adding. Remind the children to bridge to the next multiple of 10, using number facts they know: for example, 125 + 8 = 125 + 5 + 3 = 130 + 3 = 133. Encourage the children to discuss any other ways of working out the answers, such as adding 9 by adding 10 and subtracting 1.

Developing Numeracy
Mental Maths Year 3
© A & C BLACK

Hen house

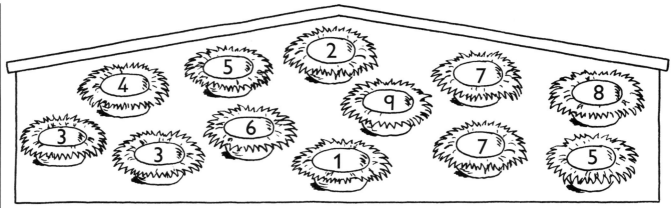

The nests hold different numbers of eggs.

• Collect **exactly** the number of eggs shown.
  Record which nests you chose.

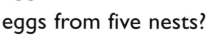

> You must take **all** the eggs from a nest.

1. Collect 26 eggs.

    $8 + 2 + 9 + 1 + 6 = 26$

2. Collect 35 eggs.

    _____

3. Collect 46 eggs.

    _____

4. Collect 53 eggs.

    _____

5. Collect 50 eggs. Only use nests with more than 2 eggs.

    _____

6. Collect 32 eggs. Only use nests with an odd number of eggs.

    _____

Now try this!

• **How many different totals can you make, if you collect:** eggs from four nests?

eggs from five nests?

Teachers' note Ensure the children understand that they must take all the eggs from a nest, not just a few of them. Encourage them to use strategies such as collecting pairs of numbers that total 9, 10 or 11, or choosing the largest numbers first before counting on. During the plenary, discuss how many different answers are possible for each question.

**Developing Numeracy
Mental Maths Year 3
© A & C BLACK**

A split and a bit

The cards show how to split numbers into | multiples of 5 | **and a bit.**

☆ Find the total for each card.

☆ Then cut out the cards. Sort them into pairs with the same total.

☆ Two cards have no matching pair. Draw two cards of your own with totals to match these cards.

35 + 18 = ____	46 + 27 = ____	37 + 27 = ____
17 + 37 = ____	37 + 37 = ____	19 + 25 = ____
37 + 26 = ____	47 + 16 = ____	38 + 26 = ____
15 + 39 = ____	35 + 38 = ____	27 + 26 = ____

Teachers' note This activity involves partitioning numbers into '5 and a bit', '15 and a bit', '25 and a bit', and so on, as a means of adding numbers with the units digits 6, 7, 8 and 9. Revise additions such as 15 + 35, 45 + 15, 35 + 15, 35 + 25 before beginning the activity.

**Developing Numeracy
Mental Maths Year 3
© A & C BLACK**

Jammy pairs

- **Colour a pair of touching numbers.**
  Split the numbers into tens and units
  to help you find the total.

Example:

(24) + (54)

20 + 4 + 50 + 4

70 + 8

= 78

22	55	38	51	35	23	57	24
43	32	57	21	17	28	41	54
18	31	46	53	35	14	26	31
25	52	44	48	45	29	33	42

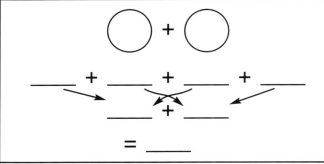

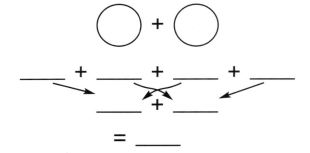

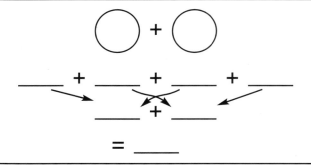

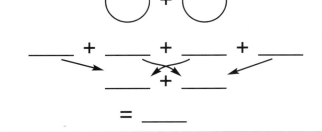

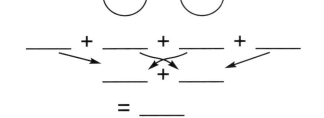

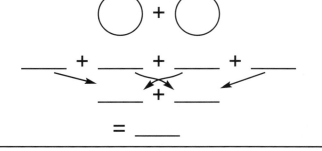

- **Find pairs of touching numbers which total:**

49   75   87   61   96   95   43

Teachers' note Revise partitioning into tens and units at the start of the lesson. Demonstrate what happens when the two units digits add to more than 10: for example, 38 + 26 = 30 + 8 + 20 + 6 = 50 + 14 = 64. Some children may find it helpful to partition the numbers using place value (arrow) cards.

Developing Numeracy
Mental Maths Year 3
© A & C BLACK

20

Grand prix

- **Count up from the smaller number to find the | difference | . Write it on the flag.**

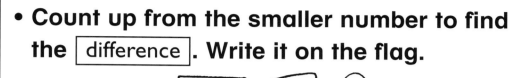

1. 503 – 496

2. 205 – 197
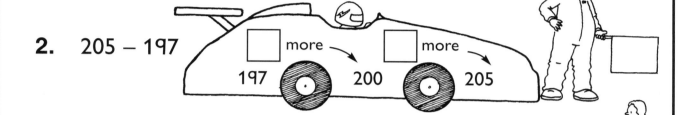

3. 304 – 295
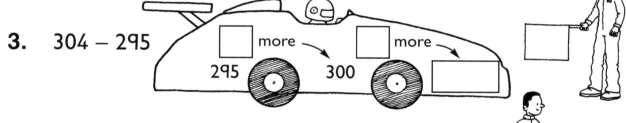

4. 406 – 391
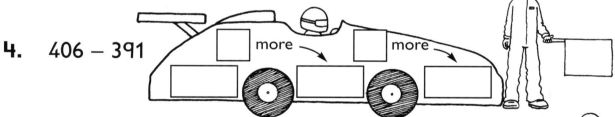

5. 609 – 588
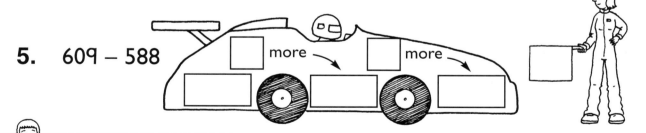

Now try this!

- **Answer these in the same way.**

809 – 789 = ____   611 – 594 = ____   701 – 686 = ____

506 – 487 = ____   907 – 890 = ____   215 – 188 = ____

915 – 885 = ____   1001 – 994 = ____   1002 – 993 = ____

Teachers' note Begin the lesson by asking the children to count up in ones from a number just below a multiple of 100 up to and beyond that multiple: for example, from 394 to 406. Then give other pairs of numbers and ask the children to say the multiple of 100 that lies between them. Draw a few racing cars on the board and demonstrate how to use them to count up through a multiple of 100.

Developing Numeracy
Mental Maths Year 3
© A & C BLACK

Near double magic

- **Find the total for each pair. Double one of the numbers, then add or subtract 1.**

1.

Double 15 and add 1.
Or, double 16 and subtract 1.

2.

3.

4.

5.

6.

7.

8.

9.

10.

11.

12.

13.

- **Discuss with a partner how to answer these questions using doubles. Make notes and find the answers.**

  299 + 300   500 + 499   251 + 250   1000 + 999

Teachers' note The children will need to know by heart, or be able to derive quickly, doubles of numbers to 20 and doubles of multiples of 5 to 100. The activity on page 36 could be used to revise these facts before starting this sheet. Encourage the children to explain each calculation strategy aloud to a partner. Use a range of vocabulary to reinforce addition and doubling words.

Developing Numeracy
Mental Maths Year 3
© A & C BLACK

Fleas jumping

• **Use multiples of 10 to help you work out the answers.**

1. 54 + 29 = $\boxed{83}$

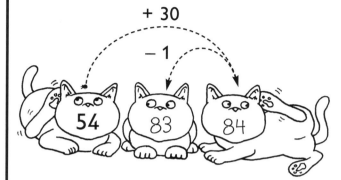

+ 30
− 1
54   83   84

2. 25 + 39 = $\boxed{}$

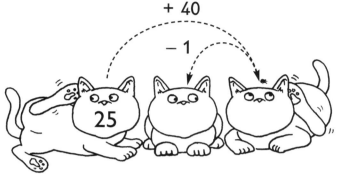

+ 40
− 1
25

3. 56 − 29 = $\boxed{}$

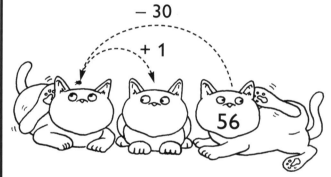

− 30
+ 1
56

4. 72 − 39 = $\boxed{}$

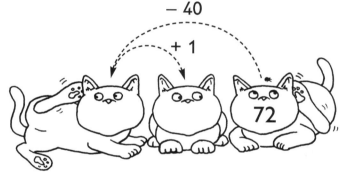

− 40
+ 1
72

5. 86 + 59 = $\boxed{}$

+
−
86

6. 63 − 38 = $\boxed{}$

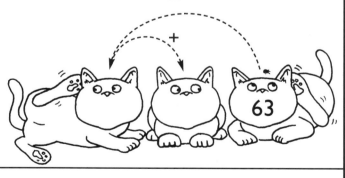

−
+
63

Now try this!

• **Work out the answers in your head.**

55 + 39 = _____	26 + 59 = _____	74 − 29 = _____
87 − 49 = _____	46 + 28 = _____	62 − 28 = _____
25 + 47 = _____	96 − 58 = _____	82 − 47 = _____

Teachers' note Ensure that the children are confident in adding and subtracting multiples of 10 to/from any two-digit number before starting this activity. Point out that some questions are additions and others are subtractions, and discuss how to adjust after adding or subtracting the multiple of 10.

Developing Numeracy
Mental Maths Year 3
© A & C BLACK

Motorbike maze game

- ## Play this game with a partner.

☆ **You need** a dice and two small counters.

☆ Take turns to roll the dice and move your counter. Work out the question and find the answer further along the track. Move your counter to this square and wait until your next turn to roll the dice again.

☆ The first player to land on a WIN square is the winner.

start						
245 + 9	427 − 9	585 − 11	254 + 11	418 + 11	276 + 9	579 − 11
441 + 9	234 − 11	553 − 9	430 + 11	574 + 9	436 − 11	285 − 11
544 − 11	421 + 9	564 − 11	243 − 9	429 + 9	570 + 9	425 + 9
223 + 9	252 − 9	256 + 11	583 − 11	265 − 9	447 − 11	568 + 9
450 + 9	575 − 11	438 + 9	572 + 9	581 − 11	267 + 9	434 − 11
232 + 9	432 − 11	566 + 9	263 − 11	423 + 9	577 − 11	274 − 11
459 − 11	241 + 9	533 + 9	448 + 9	250 WIN!	457 WIN!!	542 WIN!!!

Teachers' note When adding and subtracting 9 or 11, remind the children to add or subtract 10 and then adjust by adding or subtracting 1. As an extension activity, the children could colour the first square on the trail, colour the answer in the same colour, and continue until a win is reached. The whole grid can be coloured in this way, using three different colours.

**Developing Numeracy
Mental Maths Year 3
© A & C BLACK**

Traffic queues

- **Use the fact on the sign to help you answer the questions in the traffic queue.**
- **Explain to a partner how you worked out each answer.**

1.

14 + 13 = 27

27 − 13 = ☐   24 + 13 = ☐   14 + 23 = ☐

2.

68 − 23 = 45

68 − 13 = ☐   45 + 23 = ☐   68 − 45 = ☐

3.

25 + 26 = 51

35 + 26 = ☐   51 − 25 = ☐   25 + 16 = ☐

4.

74 − 28 = 46

64 − 28 = ☐   46 + 28 = ☐   74 − ☐ = 28

5.

37 + 54 = 91

27 + 54 = ☐   91 − 54 = ☐   ☐ + 37 = 91

- **Write addition and subtraction facts linked to this fact. Find as many as you can.**

39 + 46 = 85

Teachers' note Encourage the children to explain how they answered the questions using the original facts. Use a range of addition and subtraction vocabulary (such as 'plus', 'add', 'makes', 'altogether', 'subtract', 'minus', 'take', 'equals'). The children could be asked to write further number facts linked to those on the signs, such as 14 + 23 = 37.

Developing Numeracy
Mental Maths Year 3
© A & C BLACK

On the nose

☆ **You need** 18 counters.

☆ Choose a number from each pool. Find the total. Write the number sentence on a separate sheet of paper.

☆ If you can find the answer on a ball, cover it with a counter.

☆ Can you give each sea lion a ball?

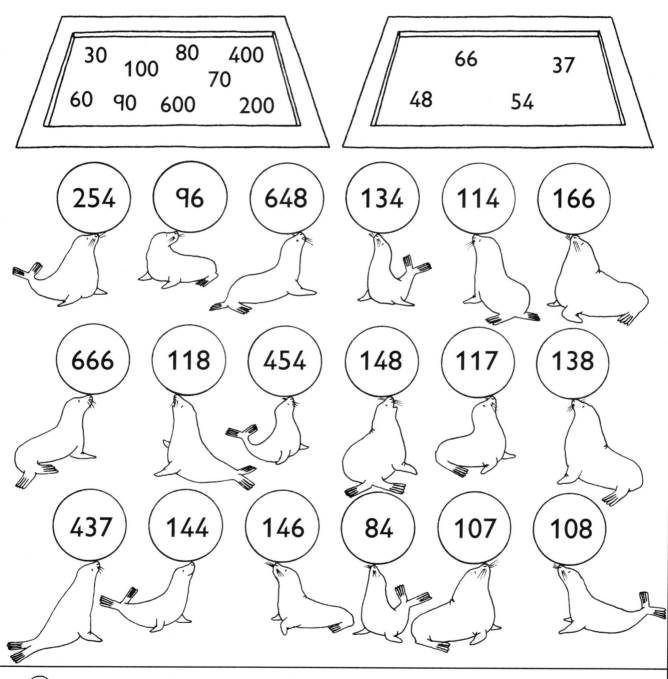

Pool 1: 30 100 80 400 70 60 90 600 200

Pool 2: 66 37 48 54

Balls:
254 96 648 134 114 166
666 118 454 148 117 138
437 144 146 84 107 108

Now try this!

• **List all the number pairs with a total between 120 and 130. Use a number from each pool.**

Teachers' note This activity explores adding multiples of 10 and 100 to two-digit numbers, including some that involve bridging 100 (such as 60 + 48 = 108). Revise adding multiples of 10 to two-digit numbers at the start of the lesson.

Developing Numeracy
Mental Maths Year 3
© A & C BLACK

Non-uniform day

To raise money for charity, these people pay £10 not to wear their uniform.

• **How much do they have left once they have paid?**

1.  She had £231.
Now she has
£ 221

2.  He had £106.
Now he has
£

3.  He had £363.
Now he has
£

4.  She had £402.
Now she has
£

• **How much money did these people have before they paid?**

5.  He had £
Now he has £91.

6.  He had £
Now he has £297.

7.  She had £
Now she has £394.

8. 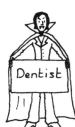 She had £
Now she has £532.

 • **Answer these questions.**

84
− 10 ——
+ 20 ——
− 40 ——
+ 70 ——

96
− 30 ——
+ 50 ——
− 60 ——
+ 80 ——

Teachers' note Encourage the children to explain which number facts they used to help them answer the questions: for example, 'I know that 107 take away 7 is 100, so 107 take away 10 must be 3 less than 100, which is 97.' Draw attention to the fact that the units digit stays the same when adding or subtracting a multiple of 10.

**Developing Numeracy
Mental Maths Year 3
© A & C BLACK**

Magic seven

- **Subtract** $\boxed{7}$ **from the middle number and add** $\boxed{7}$ **to it.**

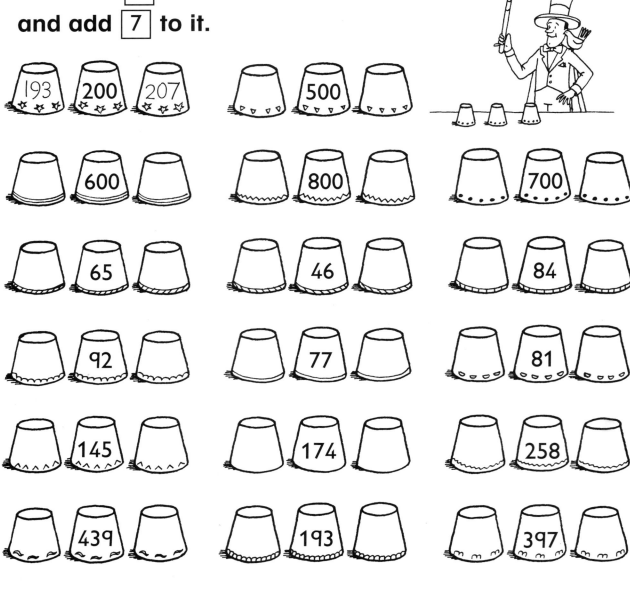

193	200	207		500				
	600			800			700	
	65			46			84	
	92			77			81	
	145			174			258	
	439			193			397	
	205			103			704	

Now try this!

- **Write additions and subtractions with odd number answers.**

Use these numbers:

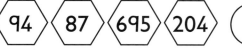

94 87 695 204 8 5 9 6

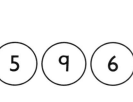

Teachers' note Encourage the children to check their answers (for example, by subtracting the smaller answer from the larger answer to see whether they get 14). For differentiation, mask the numbers on the cups and replace them with other numbers. Less confident children could be given subtractions that do not involve crossing a hundreds boundary.

**Developing Numeracy
Mental Maths Year 3
© A & C BLACK**

Snowflakes falling

• **Add each number to the number in the centre.**

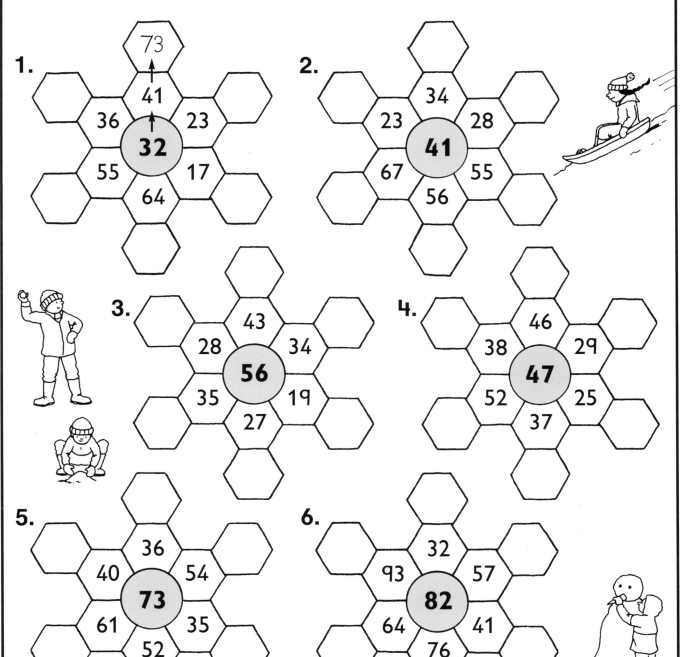

1.

73

41

36 **32** 23

55 17

64

2.

34

23 **41** 28

67 55

56

3.

43

28 **56** 34

35 19

27

4.

46

38 **47** 29

52 25

37

5.

36

40 **73** 54

61 35

52

6.

32

93 **82** 57

64 41

76

Now try this!

• **Add pairs to make totals between 110 and 140.**

28 73 57 88 66 96 87 79

Teachers' note The first two snowflakes do not involve crossing a tens or hundreds boundary, but those further down the page involve crossing first a tens boundary, and then a hundreds boundary. The children can make jottings to help them. The extension activity involves crossing both a tens and a hundreds boundary.

**Developing Numeracy
Mental Maths Year 3
© A & C BLACK**

Star makers

- **Subtract each number from the number in the centre.**

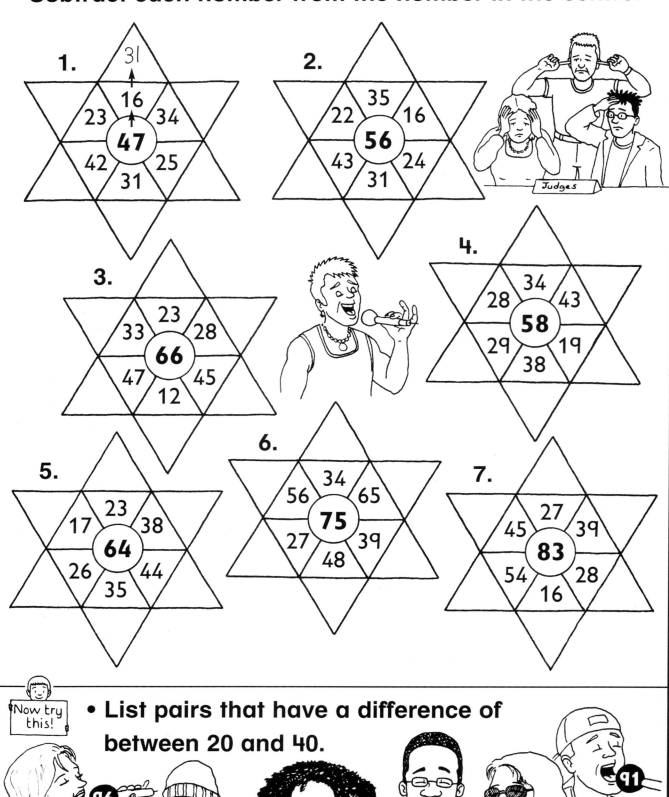

1.
31
16
23   34
47
42   25
31

2.
35
22   16
56
43   24
31

3.
23
33   28
66
47   45
12

4.
34
28   43
58
29   19
38

5.
23
17   38
64
26   44
35

6.
34
56   65
75
27   39
48

7.
27
45   39
83
54   28
16

Now try this!

- **List pairs that have a difference of between 20 and 40.**

96   38   63   48   72   91

Teachers' note The first two stars do not involve crossing a tens boundary (for example, 47 – 16 = 31), but those further down the page do (for example, 66 – 28 = 38).

Developing Numeracy
Mental Maths Year 3
© A & C BLACK

Going batty

- **Answer these multiplication and division questions as quickly as you can.**

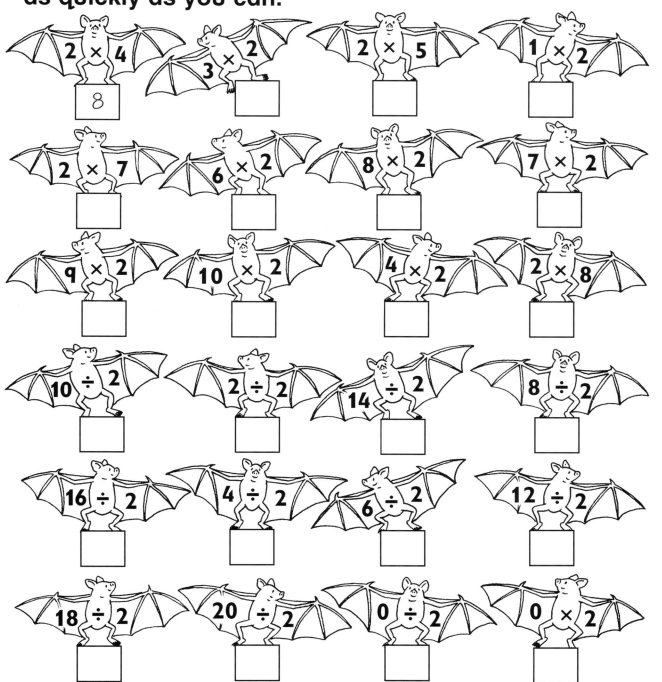

2×4 = 8

3×2 =

2×5 =

1×2 =

2×7 =

6×2 =

8×2 =

7×2 =

9×2 =

10×2 =

4×2 =

2×8 =

$10 \div 2$ =

$2 \div 2$ =

$14 \div 2$ =

$8 \div 2$ =

$16 \div 2$ =

$4 \div 2$ =

$6 \div 2$ =

$12 \div 2$ =

$18 \div 2$ =

$20 \div 2$ =

$0 \div 2$ =

0×2 =

Now try this!

- **Choose five division facts. For each one, write three statements.** Example:

$$10 \div 2 = 5$$

Half of **10** is **5**.

There are **5** twos in **10**.

10 divided by **2** is **5**.

Teachers' note During the plenary, describe the multiplication questions using vocabulary such as: 'What is double 5? What is twice 5? How many is 5 add 5? What is two lots of 5? How many is 2 times/multiplied by 5?' Describe the divisions in a similar way. Invite the children to say how they worked out the answers or whether they have learned the doubles by heart.

Developing Numeracy Mental Maths Year 3 © A & C BLACK

Pay and display

- **Work out how much money each person has. Then add to find the total.**
- **Does each family have enough for a £3 car park ticket? Tick Yes or No.**

 The machine only takes 5p and 10p coins.

1.

			PARKING £3.00
$6 \times 5p = \underline{30p}$	$8 \times 5p = \underline{}$	$5 \times 5p = \underline{}$	Ticket
$2 \times 10p = \underline{20p}$	$5 \times 10p = \underline{}$	$4 \times 10p = \underline{}$	Yes ☐ No ☐

Total $\underline{50p}$ + $\underline{}$ + $\underline{}$ = £ $\underline{}$

2.

			PARKING £3.00
$8 \times 5p = \underline{}$	$7 \times 5p = \underline{}$	$9 \times 5p = \underline{}$	Ticket
$3 \times 10p = \underline{}$	$10 \times 10p = \underline{}$	$6 \times 10p = \underline{}$	Yes ☐ No ☐

Total $\underline{}$ + $\underline{}$ + $\underline{}$ = £ $\underline{}$

3.

			PARKING £3.00
$2 \times 5p = \underline{}$	$0 \times 5p = \underline{}$	$10 \times 5p = \underline{}$	Ticket
$9 \times 10p = \underline{}$	$8 \times 10p = \underline{}$	$7 \times 10p = \underline{}$	Yes ☐ No ☐

Total $\underline{}$ + $\underline{}$ + $\underline{}$ = £ $\underline{}$

 Now try this! • **Answer these division questions.**

$40 \div 10 = \boxed{}$ $60 \div 10 = \boxed{}$ $10 \div 10 = \boxed{}$ $45 \div 5 = \boxed{}$

$30 \div 5 = \boxed{}$ $5 \div 5 = \boxed{}$ $100 \div 10 = \boxed{}$ $0 \div 10 = \boxed{}$

Teachers' note Some children may benefit from using coins and counting in fives and tens as they touch the coins. Ask children who complete the extension activity to read the questions and answers aloud using a range of vocabulary to describe the facts.

Developing Numeracy Mental Maths Year 3 © A & C BLACK

Tables tennis

• **Join each bat to its ball.**

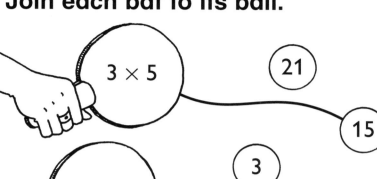

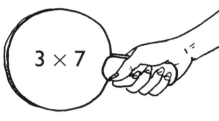

3 × 5

3 × 2

21

15

3

3 × 3

3 × 7

27

3 × 1

6

30

3 × 6

9

3 × 4

3 × 8

18

12

3 × 10

24

3 × 9

 • **Use your times tables facts to answer these.**

15 ÷ 3 = ☐   6 ÷ 3 = ☐   9 ÷ 3 = ☐   3 ÷ 3 = ☐

21 ÷ 3 = ☐   12 ÷ 3 = ☐   30 ÷ 3 = ☐   24 ÷ 3 = ☐

18 ÷ 3 = ☐   27 ÷ 3 = ☐

• **Copy out the division facts from smallest to largest.**

Teachers' note At the start of the lesson, practise the three times table. Ask children who complete the extension activity to read the questions and answers aloud using a range of vocabulary to describe the facts.

Developing Numeracy
Mental Maths Year 3
© A & C BLACK

Topple the toy

- **Answer the questions correctly to knock the toy frogs off their stands.**

1.

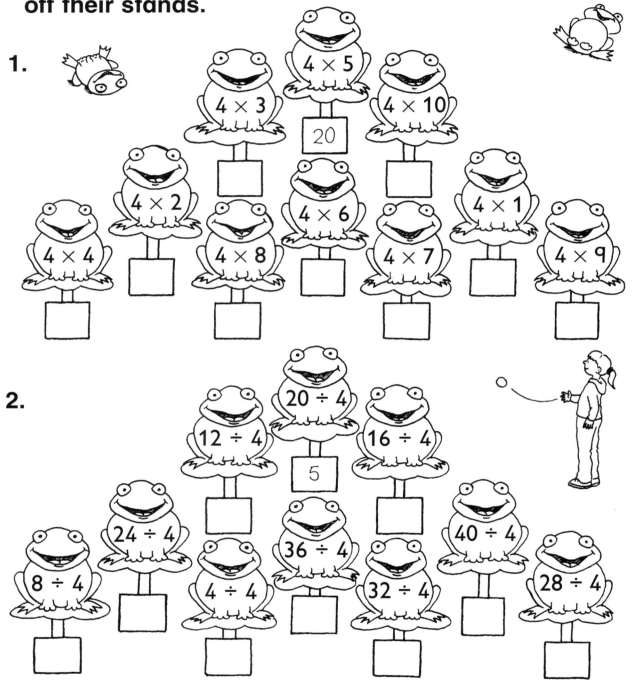

4×5

20

4×3 4×10

4×2 4×6 4×1

4×4 4×8 4×7 4×9

2.

$20 \div 4$

5

$12 \div 4$ $16 \div 4$

$24 \div 4$ $36 \div 4$ $40 \div 4$

$8 \div 4$ $4 \div 4$ $32 \div 4$ $28 \div 4$

Now try this!

You need a set of 0–9 number cards and a timer.

- ☆ Shuffle the cards. Start the timer and turn over the cards one at a time. Multiply each number by **4**.
- ☆ Repeat the activity. Try to beat your first time.

Teachers' note This activity involves using the four times table and related division facts. Some children may find it helpful to count on in fours from zero along a number line to revise multiples of 4. The children could be introduced to the 'double, double' method of multiplying by four (see page 37).

**Developing Numeracy
Mental Maths Year 3
© A & C BLACK**

Chain gang

- ## Follow these rules to make different number chains.

☆ Start with a number from 20 to 40.
If the number is odd, add one.
If the number is even, halve it.

☆ Keep going until you reach the number 1.

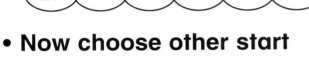

(35)(36)(18)(9)(10)( )( )( )( )( )( )( )

(39)( )( )( )( )( )( )( )( )( )

(27)( )( )( )( )( )( )( )

- ## Now choose other start numbers from 20 to 40.

What are the longest and shortest chains you can make?

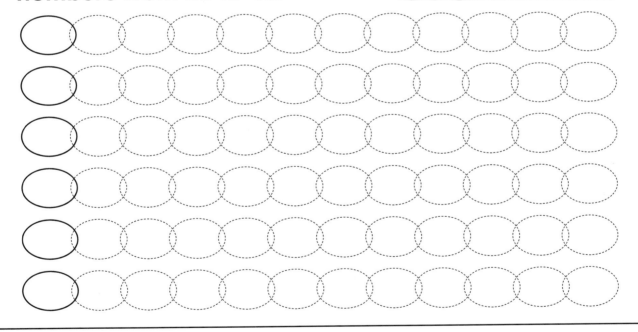

Now try this!

- ## Draw chains for all the start numbers from 20 to 40. Group them by the number of links in the chain.

35 has 11 links.

- ## What do you notice?

Teachers' note Begin the lesson by revising doubles of numbers to 20. Discuss that halving is the opposite of doubling. Go through the rules of the activity carefully, reminding the children how to recognise odd and even numbers.

**Developing Numeracy
Mental Maths Year 3
© A & C BLACK**

On the double

- Double each number.

| 11 | 22 | 14 | | 18 | | 13 | |

| 17 | | 19 | | 70 | | 90 | |

| 80 | | 35 | | 65 | | 75 | |

| 95 | | 150 | | 450 | | 350 | |

Now try this!

- Halve the amounts in these recipes.

500 g sugar	_____ sugar	190 g sugar	_____ sugar
150 g flour	_____ flour	900 g flour	_____ flour
70 g butter	_____ butter	90 g butter	_____ butter
170 g cocoa	_____ cocoa	34 g cocoa	_____ cocoa
38 ml milk	_____ milk	700 ml milk	_____ milk
130 ml water	_____ water	110 ml water	_____ water

Teachers' note During the plenary, describe the questions using vocabulary such as: 'What is double 15? What is twice 15? How many is 15 add 15? What is two lots of 15? How many is 2 times/multiplied by 15?' Invite the children to say how they worked out the answers or whether they have learned the doubles and corresponding halves by heart.

**Developing Numeracy
Mental Maths Year 3
© A & C BLACK**

Dinosaur fours

To [multiply] a number [by 4], double the number, then double the answer.

- **Use doubling to work out how many legs are in each dinosaur family.**

1.

Double 6 = 12

Double 12 = 24

$$6 \times 4 = 24$$

2.

Double 8 = ____

Double ____ = ____

$$8 \times 4 =$$

3.

Double 7 = ____

Double ____ = ____

$$7 \times 4 =$$

4.

Double 9 = ____

Double ____ = ____

$$9 \times 4 =$$

- **Answer these in the same way.**

5. $15 \times 4 =$ ____   **6.** $25 \times 4 =$ ____   **7.** $30 \times 4 =$ ____

8. $13 \times 4 =$ ____   **9.** $35 \times 4 =$ ____   **10.** $40 \times 4 =$ ____

Now try this!

To [divide] a number [by 4], halve the number, then halve the answer.

- **Use halving to answer these.**

Half of 28 = 14
Half of 14 = 7

$28 \div 4 =$ __7__ $36 \div 4 =$ ____ $40 \div 4 =$ ____

$120 \div 4 =$ ____ $60 \div 4 =$ ____ $180 \div 4 =$ ____

$160 \div 4 =$ ____ $300 \div 4 =$ ____ $500 \div 4 =$ ____

Teachers' note The children will need to know by heart, or be able to derive quickly, doubles of numbers to 20, doubles of multiples of 5 to 100 and doubles of multiples of 50 to 500, and the corresponding halves. The activity on page 36 could be completed before introducing the doubling and halving strategies here. Encourage the children to check doubling by halving, and vice versa.

Developing Numeracy
Mental Maths Year 3
© A & C BLACK

Keep doubling!

- **Double the arrow number in the question and double the answer to make a new fact. Keep going.**

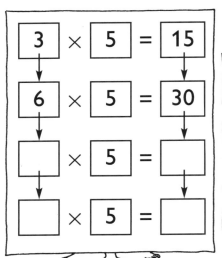

$3 \times 5 = 15$

$6 \times 5 = 30$

$\square \times 5 = \square$

$\square \times 5 = \square$

$25 \times 2 = 50$

$25 \times 4 = \square$

$\square \times \square = \square$

$\square \times \square = \square$

$\square \times \square = \square$

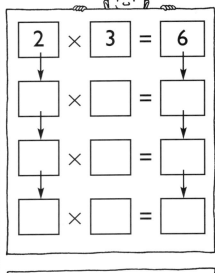

$2 \times 3 = 6$

$\square \times \square = \square$

$\square \times \square = \square$

$\square \times \square = \square$

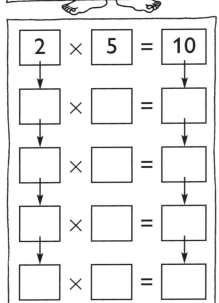

$2 \times 5 = 10$

$\square \times \square = \square$

$\square \times \square = \square$

$\square \times \square = \square$

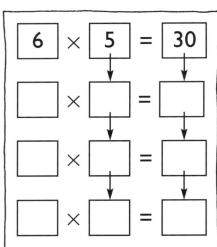

$6 \times 5 = 30$

$\square \times \square = \square$

$\square \times \square = \square$

$\square \times \square = \square$

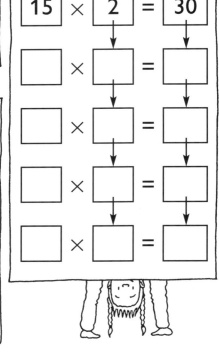

$15 \times 2 = 30$

$\square \times \square = \square$

$\square \times \square = \square$

$\square \times \square = \square$

- **Start with this fact:** $32 \times 5 = 160$.
  Halve the first number in the question. Halve the answer. $32 \times 5 = 160$
- **Keep going until you get 2 as the first number.**

Teachers' note The children will need to know by heart, or be able to derive quickly, doubles of numbers to 20, doubles of multiples of 5 and doubles of multiples of 50. The activity on page 36 could be completed before introducing the doubling and halving strategies here. Encourage the children to check doubling by halving, and vice versa.

**Developing Numeracy
Mental Maths Year 3
© A & C BLACK**

Robot statements

• **Use the numbers on the robot to make two multiplication and two division statements.**

1.
5 6
30

$5 \times 6 = 30$
$6 \times 5 = 30$
$30 \div 6 = 5$
$30 \div 5 = 6$

2.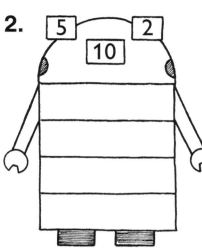
5 2
10

3.
3 4
12

4.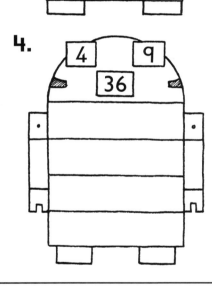
4 9
36

5.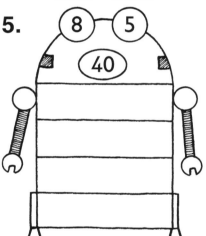
8 5
40

6.
3 7
21

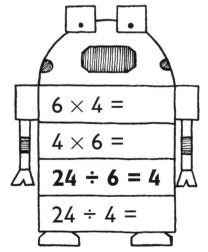

Now try this!

• **Complete the linked statements on each robot.**

3 × 8 = 24	6 × 4 =	9 × 5 =
8 × 3 =	4 × 6 =	5 × 9 =
24 ÷ 8 =	**24 ÷ 6 = 4**	45 ÷ 9 =
24 ÷ 3 =	24 ÷ 4 =	**45 ÷ 5 = 9**

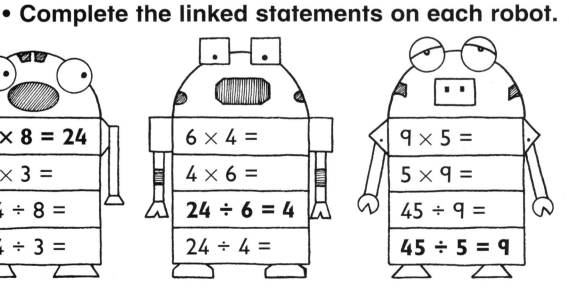

Teachers' note Help the children to see the link between the multiplication facts and division facts. Use a range of vocabulary to describe the facts and invite the children to read the questions and answers aloud. Point out that, with whole numbers, the largest number in a multiplication statement is the answer, and with division, the largest number is the first number.

Developing Numeracy
Mental Maths Year 3
© A & C BLACK

Moving digits

- **Cut along all the dotted lines. Make the machine.**
- **Slide the number strips to show what happens when you multiply these numbers by 10 and by 100:**

24   30   18   90   55   67   49

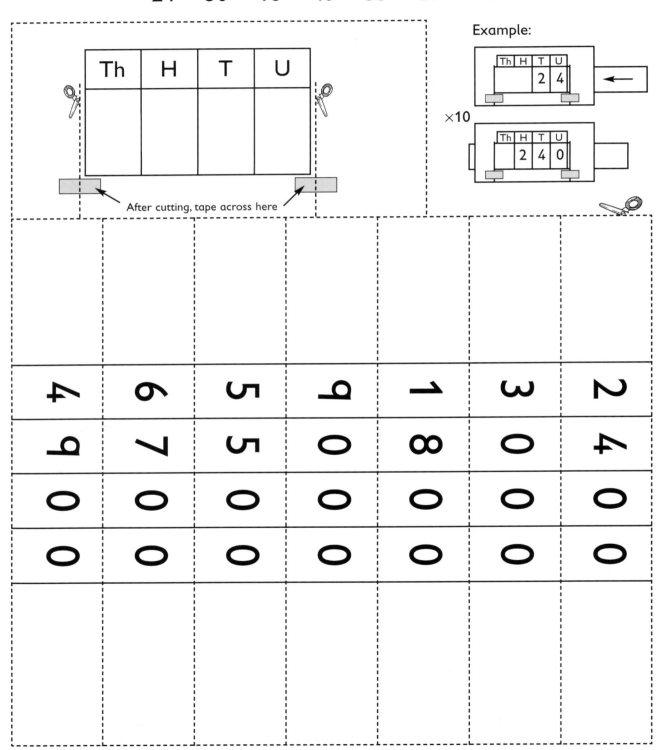

After cutting, tape across here

Example:

×10

Teachers' note Photocopy this sheet onto card. Help the children to construct the machine and insert a number strip. Demonstrate how to move the strip to the left when multiplying by 10 and 100 (and later to the right when dividing by 10 and 100). After completing the multiplications, the children can investigate what happens when the four-digit numbers are divided by 10 and 100.

**Developing Numeracy
Mental Maths Year 3
© A & C BLACK**

Zero Hero

All these answers are incorrect.

- **Be a Zero Hero! Correct the answers by crossing off zeros or writing extra zeros.**

$2 \times 10 = 200$ $5 \times 100 = 500$ $9 \times 10 = 9$

$4 \times 100 = 40$ $6 \times 10 = 6000$ $8 \times 10 = 800$

$11 \times 10 = 1100$ $13 \times 100 = 130$ $15 \times 10 = 1500$

$22 \times 100 = 220$ $25 \times 100 = 250$ $24 \times 10 = 24$

$37 \times 10 = 37$ $49 \times 10 = 4900$ $65 \times 100 = 650$

$89 \times 100 = 890$ $72 \times 100 = 72$ $53 \times 10 = 53$

$10 \times 10 = 1000$ $20 \times 10 = 20$ $40 \times 10 = 4$

$60 \times 100 = 60$ $80 \times 100 = 800$ $90 \times 100 = 9$

$200 \div 10 = 20$ $500 \div 100 = 50$ $900 \div 10 = 9$

$400 \div 10 = 4$ $60 \div 10 = 60$ $800 \div 100 = 80$

$110 \div 10 = 110$ $1300 \div 10 = 13$ $170 \div 10 = 170$

$250 \div 10 = 250$ $5300 \div 100 = 530$ $4900 \div 10 = 49$

$940 \div 10 = 940$ $6200 \div 100 = 620$ $6000 \div 100 = 6$

$8000 \div 10 = 80$ $5000 \div 100 = 500$ $2000 \div 10 = 20$

Now try this!

- **Write three multiplication statements and three division statements, each with the answer** $\boxed{30}$.

Teachers' note It is important that the children appreciate that it is the digits that move to the left or right when multiplying or dividing by 10 or 100. The children could use the 'machine' on page 40 to help them with this activity. This will ensure they appreciate that zeros are used as a place holder, to indicate the columns that are empty.

**Developing Numeracy
Mental Maths Year 3
© A & C BLACK**

Digit decisions

Each box contains one digit. You can
read numbers across and down, like this:

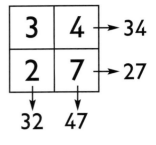

3	4
2	7

→ 34
→ 27
↓ ↓
32 47

• Fill in the missing digits.
  Then write questions
  in the blank arrows.

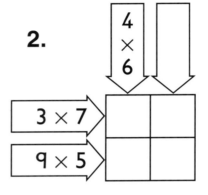

1.

| 3 × 5 | 4 × 5 |

| 3 × 4 ⟩ | 1 | 2 |
| 5 × 10 ⟩ | | |

2.

4 × 6

| 3 × 7 ⟩ | | |
| 9 × 5 ⟩ | | |

3.

3 × 5

| 6 × 3 ⟩ | | |
| 5 × 10 ⟩ | | |

4.

4 × 9   5 × 4

| 4 × 8 ⟩ | | |
| ⟩ | | |

5.

24 × 2

| 5 × 9 ⟩ | | |
| 10 × 8 ⟩ | | |

6.

3 × 4   2 × 14

| 6 × 2 ⟩ | | |
| ⟩ | | |

7.

| 5 × 5 ⟩ | | |
| 4 × 10 ⟩ | | |

8.

| 2 × 7 ⟩ | | |
| 11 × 5 ⟩ | | |

9.

| 11 × 3 ⟩ | | |
| 5 × 5 ⟩ | | |

Now try this!

• **Make up two more puzzles like these.**

Teachers' note Encourage the children to see the link between counting in fives, the multiplication
facts and division facts. Use a range of vocabulary to describe the facts and invite the children
to read the questions and answers aloud. Remind them that the order of multiplication does not
matter (for example, 3 × 5 has the same answer as 5 × 3).

**Developing Numeracy
Mental Maths Year 3
© A & C BLACK**

Follow the snakes

- **Fill in the multiplication grid to help you with the snakes below.**

×	10	20	30	40	50
2	20				
3					
4					
5					
10					

- **Follow the instructions on each snake. Write the finish number in the box.**

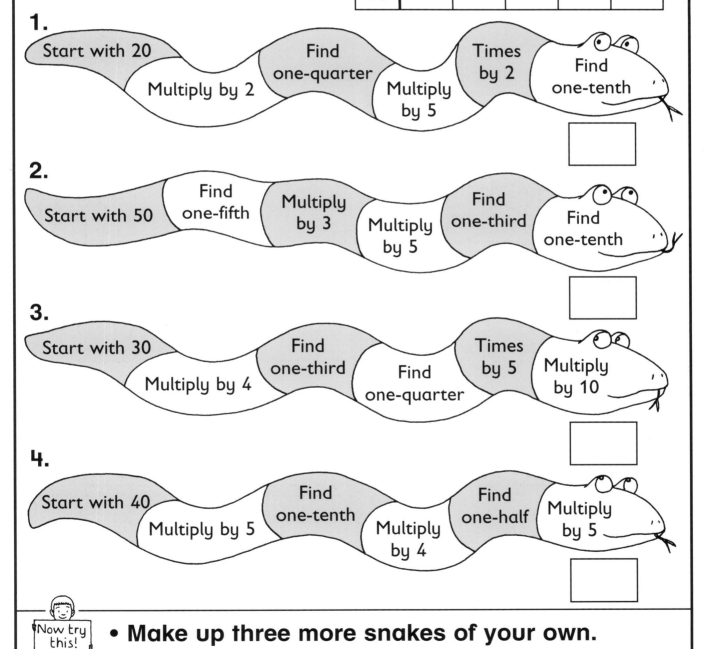

1. Start with 20 — Multiply by 2 — Find one-quarter — Multiply by 5 — Times by 2 — Find one-tenth ▢

2. Start with 50 — Find one-fifth — Multiply by 3 — Multiply by 5 — Find one-third — Find one-tenth ▢

3. Start with 30 — Multiply by 4 — Find one-third — Find one-quarter — Times by 5 — Multiply by 10 ▢

4. Start with 40 — Multiply by 5 — Find one-tenth — Multiply by 4 — Find one-half — Multiply by 5 ▢

Now try this!

- **Make up three more snakes of your own.**

Teachers' note Ensure that the children understand how to fill in the grid, and revise fractions such as one-third and one-tenth. Demonstrate how to use the grid to multiply a number along the top by a number down the side. Then show how it can be used to find a fraction of a number inside the grid. Give plenty of practice orally before the children start the snakes.

Developing Numeracy Mental Maths Year 3 © A & C BLACK

- **Follow the muddy footprints. Work out each answer and colour it in the grid below. Can you spell out who dunnit?**

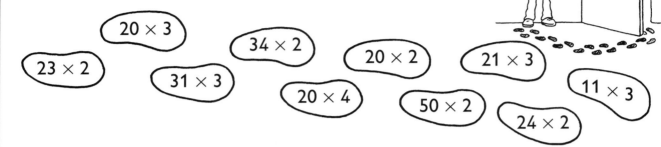

23 × 2   20 × 3   34 × 2   20 × 2   21 × 3
31 × 3   20 × 4   50 × 2   24 × 2   11 × 3

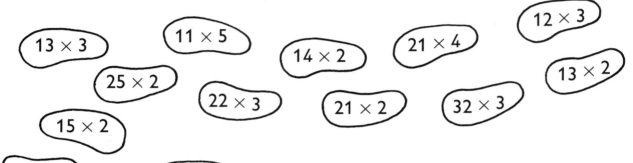

13 × 3   11 × 5   14 × 2   21 × 4   12 × 3
25 × 2   22 × 3   21 × 2   32 × 3   13 × 2
15 × 2

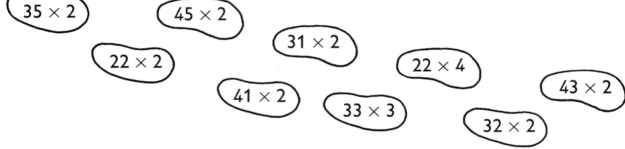

35 × 2   45 × 2   31 × 2   22 × 4   43 × 2
22 × 2   41 × 2   33 × 3   32 × 2

68	90	88	99	93	95	48	76	46	11	87	29	28
57	35	60	27	77	76	40	95	82	62	18	100	44
12	85	96	92	43	92	70	65	66	73	39	27	26
86	74	50	75	31	94	63	13	80	53	15	57	36
64	33	42	23	67	91	84	67	30	98	47	35	55

Now try this!

- **Write three different multiplications, each with the answer 36 .**

Teachers' note These multiplications do not cross tens boundaries, other than when a multiple of 5 is multiplied (for example, 35 × 2). The children may wish to partition each two-digit number before multiplying, in the following way: 34 × 2 = 30 × 2 + 4 × 2 = 60 + 8 = 68. Provide place value (arrow) cards, if necessary.

**Developing Numeracy
Mental Maths Year 3
© A & C BLACK**

Diagonal divisions

- **Divide each number in the first column by the number diagonally opposite.**
- **Tick if the divisions give the same answer.**

1.

$51 \div 10 = 5\ r\ 1$

26	10
51	5

✔

$26 \div 5 = 5\ r\ 1$

2.

33	10
63	5

3.

42	2
17	5

4.

27	3
17	5

5.

44	3
14	10

6.

17	3
13	4

7.

26	10
72	4

8.

19	10
47	3

9.

32	4
26	5

Now try this!

- **Make up three more grids where the divisions give the same answer.**

Teachers' note At the start of the lesson, revise division facts corresponding to the two, three, four, five and ten times tables, and introduce questions involving a remainder. Some children may benefit from having a list of the tables/division facts to refer to if they do not know them by heart. The children might also find it helpful to use cubes or counters when dividing.

**Developing Numeracy
Mental Maths Year 3
© A & C BLACK**

Funny photos

- **For each problem, do the division and decide whether to** round **the answer** up **or** down **.**

1. There were **32** of us at the lake. Each boat could hold **5** people. How many boats did we need?

☐ boats

2. At my party we opened a bag of **30** sweets. We got **4** sweets each. How many were at my party?

☐ children

3. There are **29** of us in my class. We had to get in **pairs**. How many pairs were there?

☐ pairs

4. I got **£26** for my birthday. I bought some CDs that cost **£5** each. How many CDs did I buy?

☐ CDs

5. There were **73** of us at camp. Each tent could sleep **10** people. How many tents did we need?

☐ tents

6. I shared **17** treats equally between our **4** new puppies. How many did each puppy get?

☐ treats

7. Dad shared **29** chocolates equally between **3** of us. How many did we each get?

☐ chocolates

Teachers' note Discuss the need to round up or down after division in certain situations. Remind the children that it is important to think about whether the answer is sensible; give examples of rounding up (where an extra boat is needed for the remainder) and of rounding down (where the remainder is not enough to buy another CD).

Developing Numeracy Mental Maths Year 3 © A & C BLACK

Answers

p 7
1. (a) Ella   (b) Ella
   (c) Asma   (d) Asma
   (e) Beth   (f) Beth
2. (a) Chloe   (b) Kim
   (c) Leah   (d) Ella
   (e) Kim   (f) Beth

Now try this!
92, 76, 60, 44, 28, 12

p 9

①			②		③				⑤	
31			47	④—57	54	51	48	45	42
⑥—28	33	38	43	48	53		⑦		47
25			39		49	⑧—59	54	49	44
22	⑪	⑨ 35	40	45	50	55		51	
⑩—19	23	27	31		41		51		⑫
16		32	⑬—32	37	42	47	52	57	62
13		37		33		43			58
10		42	⑭—24	29	34	39			54
⑮—7	27	47	67		⑯—35	40	45	50	

Now try this!
Rule: count on in 5s

p 11
Now try this!
494   499   500

p 12
Missing numbers:
743   858   799

p 13
1. 408 436 503 593 699
2. 78 280 312 409 534
3. 69 399 498 718 721
4. 198 507 523 692 854
5. 93 395 539 650 768
6. 678 687 768 786 867

p 15
1. 5
   6
   3
   8
2. 3   3. 12
   15   8
   11   4
   18   2
4. 15   5. 3
   3   12
   0   6
   7   2
6. 2   7. 6
   9   5
   8   3
   4   1
8. 5   9. 10
   3   14
   6   9
   4   2

p 17
1. 145 ml   2. 181 ml
3. 371 ml   4. 445 ml
5. 741 ml   6. 613 ml
7. 903 ml   8. 1001 ml

Now try this!
Totals:
318   640   535
323   645   540
321   643   538
325   647   542

p 20
Now try this!
49 = 18 + 31
75 = 33 + 42
87 = 55 + 32
61 = 43 + 18
96 = 52 + 44
95 = 41 + 54
43 = 14 + 29
There may be other possible answers.

p 21
1. 7   2. 8   3. 9   4. 15   5. 21

Now try this!
20   17   15
19   17   27
30   7   9

p 22
1. 31
2. 99   3. 61   4. 119
5. 159   6. 91   7. 51
8. 69   9. 109   10. 179
11. 129 12. 151 13. 169

p 23
1. 83   2. 64
3. 27   4. 33
5. 145   6. 25

Now try this!
94   85   45
38   74   34
72   38   35

p 25
1. 14   37   37
2. 55   68   23
3. 61   26   41
4. 36   74   46
5. 81   37   54

p 26
Now try this!
60 + 66 = 126
70 + 54 = 124
80 + 48 = 128
90 + 36 = 127

p 27
1. £221   2. £96
3. £353   4. £392
5. £101   6. £307
7. £404   8. £542

Now try this!
74   66
104   146
44   36
154   176

p 28
193 200 207   493 500 507   693 700 707
593 600 607   793 800 807   77 84 91
58 65 72   39 46 53   74 81 88
85 92 99   70 77 84   251 258 265
138 145 152   167 174 181   390 397 404
432 439 446   186 193 200   697 704 711
198 205 212   96 103 110

p 29

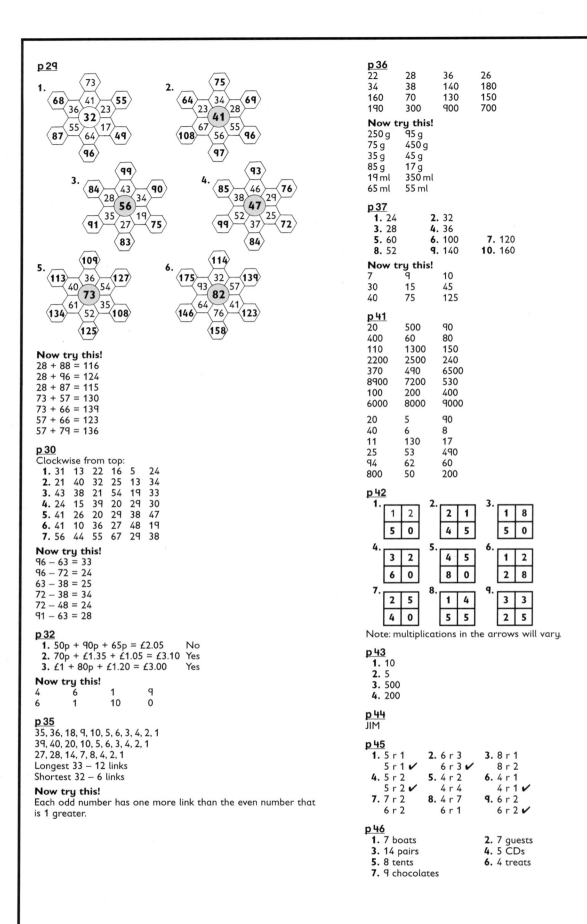

1. 73, 68, 41, 55, 36, 23, 32, 87, 55, 17, 49, 64, 96

2. 75, 64, 34, 69, 23, 28, 41, 108, 67, 56, 96, 97

3. 99, 84, 43, 90, 28, 34, 56, 91, 35, 19, 75, 27, 83

4. 93, 85, 46, 76, 38, 29, 47, 99, 52, 25, 72, 37, 84

5. 109, 113, 36, 127, 40, 54, 73, 134, 61, 35, 108, 52, 125

6. 114, 175, 32, 139, 93, 57, 82, 146, 64, 41, 123, 76, 158

Now try this!
28 + 88 = 116
28 + 96 = 124
28 + 87 = 115
73 + 57 = 130
73 + 66 = 139
57 + 66 = 123
57 + 79 = 136

p 30

Clockwise from top:
1. 31 13 22 16 5 24
2. 21 40 32 25 13 34
3. 43 38 21 54 19 33
4. 24 15 39 20 29 30
5. 41 26 20 29 38 47
6. 41 10 36 27 48 19
7. 56 44 55 67 29 38

Now try this!
96 − 63 = 33
96 − 72 = 24
63 − 38 = 25
72 − 38 = 34
72 − 48 = 24
91 − 63 = 28

p 32

1. 50p + 90p + 65p = £2.05   No
2. 70p + £1.35 + £1.05 = £3.10   Yes
3. £1 + 80p + £1.20 = £3.00   Yes

Now try this!
4   6   1   9
6   1   10   0

p 35

35, 36, 18, 9, 10, 5, 6, 3, 4, 2, 1
39, 40, 20, 10, 5, 6, 3, 4, 2, 1
27, 28, 14, 7, 8, 4, 2, 1
Longest 33 – 12 links
Shortest 32 – 6 links

Now try this!
Each odd number has one more link than the even number that is 1 greater.

p 36

22	28	36	26
34	38	140	180
160	70	130	150
190	300	900	700

Now try this!
250 g   95 g
75 g   450 g
35 g   45 g
85 g   17 g
19 ml   350 ml
65 ml   55 ml

p 37

1. 24   **2.** 32
3. 28   **4.** 36
5. 60   **6.** 100   **7.** 120
8. 52   **9.** 140   **10.** 160

Now try this!
7   9   10
30   15   45
40   75   125

p 41

20	500	90
400	60	80
110	1300	150
2200	2500	240
370	490	6500
8900	7200	530
100	200	400
6000	8000	9000
20	5	90
40	6	8
11	130	17
25	53	490
94	62	60
800	50	200

p 42

1. 12 / 50
2. 21 / 45
3. 18 / 50
4. 32 / 60
5. 45 / 80
6. 12 / 28
7. 25 / 40
8. 14 / 55
9. 33 / 25

Note: multiplications in the arrows will vary.

p 43

1. 10
2. 5
3. 500
4. 200

p 44

JIM

p 45

1. 5 r 1   **2.** 6 r 3   **3.** 8 r 1
5 r 1 ✔   6 r 3 ✔   8 r 2
4. 5 r 2   **5.** 4 r 2   **6.** 4 r 1
5 r 2 ✔   4 r 4   4 r 1 ✔
7. 7 r 2   **8.** 4 r 7   **9.** 6 r 2
6 r 2   6 r 1   6 r 2 ✔

p 46

1. 7 boats   **2.** 7 guests
3. 14 pairs   **4.** 5 CDs
5. 8 tents   **6.** 4 treats
7. 9 chocolates